The Best Of Alex 2005

𝕿𝖍𝖊 𝕯𝖆𝖎𝖑𝖞 𝕿𝖊𝖑𝖊𝖌𝖗𝖆𝖕𝖍

Charles Peattie & Russell Taylor

Masterley Publishing

The Best Of
Alex
2005

Copyright © 2004-2005 Charles Peattie and Russell Taylor

The right of Charles Peattie and Russell Taylor to be identified as the Author of the Work
has been asserted by them in accordance with the Copyright, Designs and Patents Act 1988.

First published by MASTERLEY PUBLISHING

All rights reserved. No part of this publication may be reproduced, stored in retrieval system,
or transmitted, in any form or by any means without the prior written permission of the
publisher, nor be otherwise circulated in any form of binding or cover than that in which it is
published and without a similar condition being imposed on the subsequent purchaser.

Layout and Artwork: Jain Spero

Alex would like to congratulate FTSE Group on their tenth birthday and thank them and MondoVisione for their support once again.

FOREWORD

The financial world that Alex has just rejoined has become a strangely diversified place. Perhaps this is due to the belated intrusion of some sort of meritocracy, or maybe it's the rigorous application of "diversity" policies, but just about everyone under 35 in the City of London nowadays is hyper-qualified, multilingual and ... well ... foreign.

Obviously as satirists of the modern business world we could hardly ignore this trend, so the character of Christian was introduced in the interests of socio-economic accuracy (plus of course the fact that a bit of French bashing always goes down well with a British audience).

But should we be going further in pandering to the "new" City? Should we run the cartoon in Italian or German on alternate weeks? Or publish next year's annual collection in the form of a spreadsheet? Should Alex start sporting a pullover and drive a scooter into work?

Thankfully the older generation is still there in respectable numbers. But, hold on ... didn't you guys tell us that you'd have retired by the time you were forty? So what went wrong? Declining bonuses? Increasing material aspirations? School fees? The necessity of keeping up with that hedge fund manager next door..?

This of course is that peculiar variety of the mid-life crisis that is unique to the City. Well, if it's any consolation we're glad you're still there. After all we rely on you to feed us your increasingly bitter and cynical ideas. So, if you don't already have our contact details then you'll find them on the inside back page ... and please don't omit to stitch up those new foreign upstarts in your midst.

Charles Peattie   Russell Taylor

Charles Peattie and Russell Taylor

Clive
(Alex's new boss)

Rupert
(senior director)

Alex
(investment banker)

Penny
(Alex's wife)

Bridget
(Clive's wife)

Christopher
(Alex's son)

Christian
(Eurotrash trainee)

Panel 1: SO DO YOU FINALLY FEEL MORE COMFORTABLE IN YOUR NEW JOB, ALEX? — YES, CLIVE.

Panel 2: WHEN ONE FIRST JOINS SUCH A HUGE ORGANISATION, ONE INEVITABLY FEELS ANONYMOUS, ISOLATED, OVERLOOKED... THAT NO ONE EVEN KNOWS THAT ONE EXISTS...

Panel 3: IT CAN TAKE WEEKS TO GRADUALLY MAKE ONE'S PRESENCE KNOWN AND START TO FEEL THAT ONE'S TALENTS HAVE FINALLY BEEN ACCEPTED, ACKNOWLEDGED AND ABOVE ALL VALUED...

Panel 4: YES... I GOT MY FIRST CALL FROM A HEADHUNTER TODAY.

email: alex-cartoon@etgate.co.uk

Panel 1: I MUST ADMIT I FEEL SO MUCH HEALTHIER SINCE I STARTED CYCLING INTO WORK...

Panel 2: AND FRANKLY, THE TRANSPORT INFRASTRUCTURE OUT HERE IN DOCKLANDS IS SO POOR THAT A BICYCLE IS THE MOST PRACTICAL OPTION FOR GETTING HERE.

Panel 3: THEN OF COURSE THERE'S THE COST SAVING... PLUS THE FACT THAT ONE DOESN'T HAVE TO WORRY ABOUT THE CONGESTION CHARGE - NOT TO MENTION THE ENVIRONMENTAL BENEFITS...

Panel 4: DO YOU THINK ALEX BELIEVES ANY OF THAT RUBBISH? — NO... BUT IT'S BETTER THAN ADMITTING I DIDN'T GIVE HIM A CORPORATE CAR PARKING SPACE...

HEAD OF DEPT.

email: alex-cartoon@etgate.co.uk

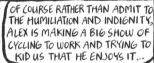

Panel 1: AS ALEX'S NEW BOSS I DIDN'T AWARD HIM A CAR PARKING SPACE AT THE BANK.

Panel 2: OF COURSE RATHER THAN ADMIT TO THE HUMILIATION AND INDIGNITY, ALEX IS MAKING A BIG SHOW OF CYCLING TO WORK AND TRYING TO KID US THAT HE ENJOYS IT...

Panel 3: BUT EVERY TIME I SEE HIS HELMET AND CAGOULE HANGING UP HERE IT REMINDS ME HOW, FOR THE FIRST TIME EVER, I'VE ACTUALLY GOT ONE OVER ON ALEX...

Panel 4: YES... WITH MY CYCLE CLOBBER ON DISPLAY IN THE OFFICE CLIVE WILL ASSUME I'M STILL THERE... — EXCELLENT... LET'S HEAD INTO TOWN FOR A FEW BEERS... TAXI!

email: alex-cartoon@etgate.co.uk

Panel 1: I MUST ADMIT I'M SURPRISED TO HEAR THAT ALEX COMPARES PRICES WHEN HE'S SHOPPING THESE DAYS... SPECIAL OFFER

Panel 2: YOU MUSN'T FORGET THAT HE SPENT A YEAR OUT OF WORK WHEN HE DIDN'T HAVE ALL THE ADVANTAGES OF BEING ON A BANKER'S SALARY... GAP

Panel 3: NOW THAT HE'S BACK IN EMPLOYMENT IT'S INEVITABLE THAT SOME HABITS WILL DIE HARD... FINANCIAL PRUDENCE?

Panel 4: NO, OSTENTATIOUSNESS... ACCORDING TO MY BRAND NEW STATE OF THE ART BLACKBERRY I CAN GET THIS TOASTER £5 CHEAPER ON LINE... TOASTER

email: alex-cartoon@etgate.co.uk

Alex PEATTIE + TAYLOR

OF COURSE WE HAVE THREE CARS. EVERYONE IN OUR STREET IN WANDSWORTH HAS AT LEAST THAT MANY.

MY HUSBAND NEEDS ONE, AS DO I, AND OF COURSE OUR LIVE-IN NANNY HAS TO HAVE ONE...

YOU PROVIDE YOUR NANNY WITH A CAR?

WELL, ONE HAS TO...FRANKLY WE WORK HER SO HARD SHE HARDLY EVER GETS A CHANCE TO USE IT, BUT HER HAVING HER OWN VEHICLE IS VERY PRACTICAL.

CLAIRE, WOULD YOU MOVE YOUR CAR SO I CAN HAVE YOUR PARKING SPACE OUTSIDE THE HOUSE?

SO I HAVE TO DRIVE ROUND FOR HOURS LOOKING FOR ANOTHER ONE AS USUAL?

email: alex-cartoon@etgate.co.uk

Alex PEATTIE + TAYLOR

ALEX, A CAR PARKING SPACE AT THE BANK HAS BECOME AVAILABLE. I WONDER IF YOU'D LIKE IT...?

WELL, THANK YOU, CLIVE I'D LIKE IT VERY MUCH.

IT MAKES SENSE. YOU ARE AN IMPORTANT MEMBER OF THE DEPARTMENT AFTER ALL.

YOU'VE A DIFFICULT COMMUTE INTO WORK AND IT SEEMS RIDICULOUS THAT YOU SHOULD BE RELIANT ON THE VAGARIES OF PUBLIC TRANSPORTATION...

WHICH OF COURSE WOULD GIVE YOU AN EXCUSE FOR NOT BEING ABLE TO MAKE THE MORNING MEETING WHICH I'VE JUST PUT FORWARD TO 6.45 AM...

HEE HEE...

WHAT?!

email: alex-cartoon@etgate.co.uk

Alex PEATTIE + TAYLOR

BACK IN THE OLD DAYS WE BROKERS KNEW WHERE WE STOOD WITH OUR CLIENTS, ALEX...

THEY'D BE MANAGING MONEY ON BEHALF OF COMPANY PENSION FUNDS OR LOCAL COUNCILS AND THEY'D BE LOOKING FOR LONG TERM, LOW RISK STRATEGIES...

BUT MANY OF OUR CLIENTS ARE NOW HIGHLY-GEARED HEDGE FUNDS - INVESTING MONEY FOR HYPER-RICH INDIVIDUALS ON A SHORT TERM HIGH RISK BASIS. IT REQUIRES A WHOLE NEW APPROACH FROM US...

I CAN IMAGINE...

I MEAN HOW DOES ONE TALK DOWN TO A CLIENT WHO EARNS MORE THAN ONESELF?

IT MUST BE VERY GALLING FOR YOU...

email: alex-cartoon@etgate.co.uk

Alex PEATTIE + TAYLOR

HEDGE FUNDS ARE WHERE THE BUSINESS IS THESE DAYS, ALEX, AND I'VE GOT A CONTACT IN A START-UP THAT'S DOING REALLY WELL

EXCELLENT. SO YOU WANT ME TO TAKE HIM OUT FOR A GOOD LUNCH, A COUPLE OF BOTTLES OF CLARET...?

ACTUALLY THERE'S A DIFFERENT WORK ETHIC IN THE CITY THESE DAYS...

KNOWING THIS GUY, HE'S MORE LIKELY TO WANT TO MEET IN HIS OFFICE AND SEND OUT FOR SANDWICHES...

WELL, I CAN HANDLE THAT TOO, CLIVE...

SORRY... DID I FORGET TO MENTION IT WAS ROBIN, OUR EX-GRADUATE TRAINEE? SNIGGER

THE VENGEFUL LITTLE CREEP HAS SENT ME OUT TO GET THE SANDWICHES...

TONY'S CAFÉ

email: alex-cartoon@etgate.co.uk

14

Alex PEATTIE + TAYLOR

THE SWAPS BALL IS STILL LARGELY A MALE-DOMINATED OCCASION AND THE AUCTION PRIZES TEND TO REFLECT THIS...

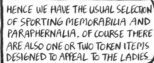

HENCE WE HAVE THE USUAL SELECTION OF SPORTING MEMORABILIA AND PARAPHERNALIA. OF COURSE THERE ARE ALSO ONE OR TWO TOKEN ITEMS DESIGNED TO APPEAL TO THE LADIES.

WELL, IN THIS HIGHLY-COMPETITIVE, TESTOSTERONE CHARGED AND ALCOHOL-FUELLED ATMOSPHERE I CAN TELL YOU WHICH AUCTION LOTS WILL GO FOR THE MOST MONEY AT THE END OF THE EVENING...

WHAT AM I BID FOR THIS HERMES HAND-BAG? £10,000... £11,000... £12,000...

WHEN YOU'RE GOING HOME WITH A FOOTBALL SHIRT OR CRICKET BAT YOU DRUNK-ENLY PAID A FORTUNE FOR YOU NEED A GIFT TO PLACATE THE WIFE...

email: alex-cartoon@etgate.co.uk

Alex PEATTIE + TAYLOR

IT'S SO ANNOYING WHEN ONE GOES OUT TO ENJOY A QUIET CUP OF COFFEE SOMEWHERE...

WAH! WAH!

AND SOME ANTISOCIAL MOTHER HAS HER SCREAMING INFANT WITH HER AND SPOILS THINGS FOR EVERYONE ELSE...

WAH!

I MEAN, I'VE GOT NOTHING AGAINST OTHER PEOPLE'S CHILDREN... BUT THERE ARE PLACES WHERE IT'S MORE APPROPRIATE TO HAVE THEM...

WAAH!

ONE OF US WILL HAVE TO HAVE A WORD WITH HER...

LIKE ON THE OTHER SIDE OF THE CAFÉ WHERE WE MAKE ALL OUR NANNIES SIT...

WAH...

email: alex-cartoon@etgate.co.uk

Alex PEATTIE + TAYLOR

ALL THIS POLITICALLY CORRECT CLAPTRAP IS GETTING OUT OF HAND IN LARGE ORGANISATIONS THESE DAYS, RUPERT...

FOR EXAMPLE, THESE DIVERSITY DIRECTIVES BY WHICH WE'RE OBLIGED TO TAKE QUOTAS OF EMPLOYEES FROM SPECIAL GROUPS. PEOPLE WHO ARE THEN EFFECTUELY UNSACKABLE.

ALL THIS MINDLESS KOWTOWING TO THE DICTATES OF P.C. CULTURE JUST MAKES IT HARDER FOR US IN MANAGEMENT TO GET RID OF PEOPLE WE CONSIDER SURPLUS TO REQUIREMENTS...

THAT'S UNTRUE AND UNFAIR, DAVID.

I'VE JUST ASKED PAUL DAVENPORT TO CHAIR OUR "WOMENS' AWARENESS" FORUM NEXT WEEK. IF THAT DOESN'T FINALLY CAUSE HIM TO CRACK AND RESIGN THEN NOTHING WILL...

email: alex-cartoon@etgate.co.uk

Alex PEATTIE + TAYLOR

DID YOU SEE WE GOT AN E-MAIL FROM OUR SUMMER INTERN?

IT SAID HOW MUCH HE ENJOYED HIS TWO MONTHS HERE AND THANKED US ALL. I SUPPOSE HE MUST HAVE LEFT LAST WEEK. I MUST ADMIT I DIDN'T NOTICE HE'D GONE...

WELL THAT'S VERY TYPICAL OF YOU, CLIVE, AND IT SAYS A LOT ABOUT YOUR ATTITUDE TO THOSE WHO ARE SUBORDINATE TO YOU...

I DIDN'T EVEN NOTICE THAT WE HAD AN INTERN IN THE FIRST PLACE...

email: alex-cartoon@etgate.co.uk

Strip 1

WELL DONE, ALEX... YOU'RE REALLY ENTERING INTO THE SPIRIT OF THE OCTOBER CLUB CHARITY DINNER.

I WANT TO THANK YOU FOR THE VERY GENEROUS FINANCIAL CONTRIBUTION YOU'VE MADE SO FAR. IT'S GOOD TO SEE OUR PEOPLE REALLY DIGGING DEEP INTO THEIR POCKETS FOR SUCH A WORTHY CAUSE...

ER... THANKS, CLIVE...

THAT WAS A NICE PSYCHOLOGICAL TOUCH, CLIVE. AS A BOSS ONE IS NEVER OFF DUTY AND AT TIMES LIKE THIS OUR SUBORDINATES LOOK TO US FOR REASSURANCE AND APPROVAL...

WHAT, WITH BONUSES COMING UP...?

EXACTLY. YOU'VE CERTAINLY MANAGED HIS EXPECTATIONS DOWN...

I ONLY PAID £40 FOR SOME RAFFLE TICKETS... WHAT'S HE TRYING TO TELL ME?

Strip 2

RUPERT, YOU PROMISED THE BANK WOULD REIMBURSE US FOR ANY AUCTION LOTS WE BOUGHT AT THE OCTOBER CLUB CHARITY DINNER LAST NIGHT...

YOU SAID IT WAS IMPORTANT TO BE SEEN TO BE SPENDING MORE THAN OUR DEADLY RIVALS AT CONTINENT BANK...

YES, A RIVALRY EXACERBATED BY OUR RECENT POACHING OF SEVERAL OF THEIR TOP PEOPLE...

AND LAST NIGHT ONCE THE INSTINCTIVE HOSTILITY HAD BEEN FUELLED BY ALCOHOL THERE WAS SOME EXTREMELY COMPETITIVE AND AGGRESSIVE BIDDING GOING ON BETWEEN YOU AND JUSTIN HAWKINS...

UNTIL I REMINDED YOU THAT WE HEADHUNTED HIM LAST MONTH AND HE NOW WORKS FOR US... HOW MUCH DID YOU IDIOTS PUSH THE PRICE OF THAT FISHING WEEKEND UP TO?

ER... £11,750...

Strip 3

YOU KNOW THERE ARE 27 LANGUAGES SPOKEN ON OUR FLOOR INCLUDING RUSSIAN, HINDI, MANDARIN...

IT'S A REAL GLOBAL MELTING POT...

AND IT'S USEFUL HAVING PEOPLE TO TRANSLATE ONE'S PRESENTATION WHEN ONE'S DOING AN INTERNATIONAL ROADSHOW... OF COURSE PRETTY MUCH EVERYONE SPEAKS ENGLISH THESE DAYS...

TRUE, CLIVE, BUT TRAVELLING THE WORLD THERE ARE STILL TIMES WHEN ONE ENDS UP SOMEWHERE WHERE PRESENTING IN ENGLISH IS NOT AN OPTION...

OF COURSE, YES...

FRANCE.

QUITE... JEAN-CLAUDE, WOULD YOU TRANSLATE THIS PRESENTATION FOR THE PARIS PITCH PLEASE?

THANKS.

WE'LL USE IT AS IT IS FOR THE REST OF THE WORLD...

Strip 4

YOU KNOW, WHEN I STARTED AS AN EXECUTIVE IN THE CITY I WAS FREQUENTLY ASSUMED TO BE A SECRETARY... I HAD TO CONTEND WITH THAT KIND OF SEXISM THROUGHOUT MY CAREER...

BUT NOW I'M A FULL-TIME MUM I'M ON A LEVEL WITH ALL THESE BANKERS' WIVES WHO'VE NEVER HAD TO DO A DAY'S WORK IN THEIR LIVES... IT'S QUITE ANNOYING...

I MEET THESE WOMEN IN THE PARK WITH THEIR KIDS AND THEY SIMPLY DON'T HAVE A CLUE ABOUT FEMINISM OR ANY OF WHAT I'VE HAD TO GO THROUGH...

SO I PRETEND TO ASSUME THAT THEY'RE NANNIES TO PEE THEM OFF... HEE HEE HEE...

YOU MINX!

email: alex-cartoon@etgate.co.uk

21

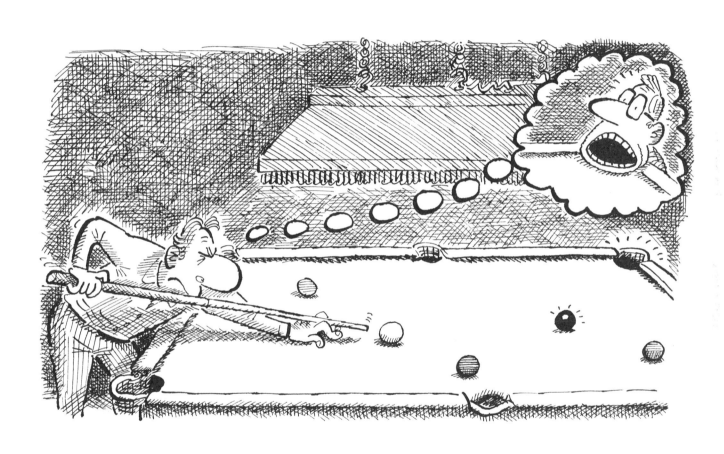

26

Strip 1

Alex — FEATTIE + TAYLOR

DAVIS, I'D LIKE YOU TO HEAD UP OUR TEAM TO GO TO THE UNIVERSITY MILKROUND NEXT WEEK...

ME? WOW!

NOW OBVIOUSLY THE IDEA IS TO ATTRACT THE BEST CALIBRE OF CANDIDATES TO COME AND WORK FOR US BY PRESENTING A THRUSTING DYNAMIC SUCCESSFUL IMAGE OF THE BANK TO THEM...

AND WE FEEL THAT YOUR PRESENCE AS A RECENT GRADUATE COULD BE THE MOST EFFECTIVE WAY OF COMMUNICATING THIS INFORMATION TO YOUNG PEOPLE...

WELL, I'M FLATTERED.

DON'T BE..WE WANT TO SHOW THAT WE'RE SO BUSY THAT WE CAN'T SPARE ANYONE OTHER THAN AN UTTER JUNIOR NON-ENTITY FOR THE OCCASION...

FINE.

email: alex-cartoon@etgate.co.uk

Strip 2

Alex — FEATTIE + TAYLOR

IT'S BONUS SEASON IN THE CITY AND EVERYBODY'S TRYING TO PLAY UP THEIR WORTH.

MOSTLY THIS INVOLVES SENDING DAILY SELF-AGGRANDISING E-MAILS TO THEIR BOSS, WHICH OF COURSE THEY ALSO C.C. TO ALL AND SUNDRY IN THE BANK

AND WHAT ABOUT YOU?

ME? GOODNESS NO... I RISE ABOVE ALL THAT TAWDRY SELF-PROMOTION... AND I CAN ONLY TRUST THAT MY DIGNIFIED RESTRAINT ON THIS FRONT WILL BE APPRECIATED IN THE RELEVANT QUARTERS...

BY YOUR BOSS?

NO, BY MY COLLEAGUES. SO THEY REALISE I'M CLEARLY ON A GUARANTEED BONUS AND DON'T HAVE TO SUCK UP TO ANYONE...

email: alex-cartoon@etgate.co.uk

Strip 3

Alex — FEATTIE + TAYLOR

THERE REALLY IS A HUGE AMOUNT OF EXTRA BUREAUCRACY IN BANKING THESE DAYS...

AFTER EVERY BUSINESS CALL WE MAKE WE HAVE TO LABORIOUSLY LOG ALL THE DETAILS OF THE CONVERSATION: WHO WE SPOKE TO, WHAT WE DISCUSSED ETC...

WELL IT'S ALL FOR THE BENEFIT OF THE CLIENT RELATIONS MANAGEMENT TEAM WHO WILL THEN PROCESS THE DATA AND ENSURE THE BANK MAKES EFFECTIVE USE OF IT...

QUITE.

...AND ALEX MASTERLEY REPORTS HAVING SPOKEN TO SIX HEADHUNTERS LAST WEEK ABOUT JOBS IN 3 OTHER BANKS...

HIS ATTEMPTS TO PRESSURISE ME INTO PAYING HIM A BIG BONUS ARE GETTING INCREASINGLY DESPERATE...

CLIENT RELATIONS MANAGEMENT

email: alex-cartoon@etgate.co.uk

Strip 4

Alex — FEATTIE + TAYLOR

CLIVE, THERE'S A GRADUATE COMING IN FOR INTERVIEW TODAY. WHO DO YOU WANT TO DO IT?

WELL, OBVIOUSLY INTERVIEWING A POTENTIAL TRAINEE IS A DULL, LOWGRADE ROUTINE PROCEDURE WHICH WOULD CLEARLY BE WELL BENEATH A HEAD OF DEPARTMENT LIKE ME...

...WHEREAS ALEX, MUCH TO HIS ANNOYANCE, IS CURRENTLY MY JUNIOR AND, AS I CAN'T RESIST ANY OPPORTUNITY TO DISCOMFORT HIM, THERE'S NO DOUBT WHO'S GOING TO GET ASSIGNED THIS PARTICULAR TASK...

SO WHY DOESN'T CLIVE WANT ME INVOLVED IN THE INTERVIEW PROCESS? IS HE HINTING THAT I MIGHT NOT HAVE A JOB BY THE TIME THAT KID STARTS...?

email: alex-cartoon@etgate.co.uk

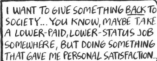

Alex
PEATTIE + TAYLOR

WHY'S ALEX COMING INTO THIS CABIN? HE'S SUPPOSED TO BE FLYING ECONOMY CLASS...

OH, *THAT* GENTLEMAN, SIR... HIS SILVER-TONGUED ELOQUENCE CHARMED THE CHECK-IN GIRLS INTO UPGRADING HIM...

WHAT? BUT HE'S MY JUNIOR...

YOU SHOULD BE PLEASED, SIR... IF YOU'RE HEADING OFF TO PITCH FOR BUSINESS IT MUST BE GOOD TO HAVE PEOPLE IN YOUR TEAM WHO ARE SKILLED IN THE ART OF PERSUASION AND SELF-PROMOTION...

YOU MUST BE JOKING?!

I'VE BEEN DELIVERING CONSISTENTLY HIGH-QUALITY SERVICE TO MY CLIENTS AND I AM CONFIDENT AN ENLIGHTENED BOSS LIKE YOU WILL REFLECT THIS IN MY BONUS...

FOUR MORE HOURS OF THIS.... SIGH

email: alex-cartoon@etgate.co.uk

Alex
PEATTIE + TAYLOR

LONG DISTANCE BUSINESS MEETINGS HAVE TRADITIONALLY BEEN CONDUCTED OVER AUDIO TELEPHONE LINK-UPS.

BY CONTRAST, VIDEO CONFERENCING WAS ALWAYS THE POOR RELATION; FOR MANY YEARS BLIGHTED BY JERKY LOW-RESOLUTION IMAGES AND SLOW TRANSMISSION TIMES...

OF COURSE THE ARRIVAL OF MODERN ULTRA-FAST INTERNET CONNECTIONS, CAPABLE OF DELIVERING HIGH-QUALITY VISUAL DATA HAS HAD SIGNIFICANT IMPLICATIONS FOR BUSINESS CONFERENCING...

YES...

WE CAN NOW PLAY INTERACTIVE WEB GAMES, DOWNLOAD MOVIE TRAILERS ETC, WHILE LISTENING TO AMERICAN LAWYERS DRONING ON...

AND AN *AUDIO* LINK MEANS THEY CAN'T SEE US DOING IT...

email: alex-cartoon@etgate.co.uk

Alex
PEATTIE + TAYLOR

"E-mail from: Alex Masterley. Hi Mum, for once you won't need to tell me off about being a lousy father to Christopher..."

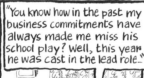

"You know how in the past my business commitments have always made me miss his school play? Well, this year he was cast in the lead role..."

"...and you'll be glad to hear that I made a special effort and managed to get along to the performance... Well, must sign off now as I've got several urgent business e-mails to write. Love Alex..."

"This message sent from my wireless handheld..."

TAP TAP

email: alex-cartoon@etgate.co.uk

Alex
PEATTIE + TAYLOR

PENNY'S FURIOUS BECAUSE I'M DOING SO MUCH CLIENT ENTERTAINMENT AT WEEKENDS THESE DAYS...

WELL YOU KNOW HOW IT IS: WHEN CHOOSING WHETHER TO DO HOSPITALITY EVENTS DURING WORKING HOURS OR AT THE WEEKEND, ONE HAS TO WEIGH UP WHO IS THE SOFTEST TOUCH: ONE'S BOSS OR ONE'S WIFE?

I.E.:- WHO IS MOST LIKELY TO GIVE YOU PERMISSION TO TAKE THE NECESSARY TIME OFF?

AND YOU END UP DOING WEEKENDS, ALEX? BUT YOUR BOSS IS CLIVE AND HE'S UTTERLY WET AND FECKLESS...

CORRECT.

SO HIS WIFE WON'T LET HIM GO TO ANYTHING AND I ALWAYS HAVE TO DEPUTISE FOR HIM...

SO YOU'VE GOT THE PERFECT CAST-IRON EXCUSE AND CLIVE'S SHOWN UP FOR THE WIMP HE IS...

EXACTLY...

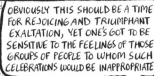

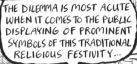

Alex PEATTIE + TAYLOR

SO HOW COME YOU KNOW WHAT YOUR GRAN'S GOT YOU FOR CHRISTMAS CHRISTOPHER?

OH, I KNOW WHERE SHE ALWAYS HIDES THE PRESENTS SO I TOOK A LOOK. OF COURSE NOW I'VE SEEN WHAT SHE'S GOT ME IT'S REALLY FRUSTRATING HAVING TO WAIT TILL CHRISTMAS DAY...

HOLD ON. BUT YOU SAID SHE'D BOUGHT YOU AN ACTION MAN AND A BART SIMPSON JIGSAW...

THAT'S RIGHT.

I POSTED THEM ON EBAY WITH DECEMBER 25TH AS THE CLOSING DATE FOR BIDS... THEY'RE ALREADY AT £23-75...

Alex PEATTIE + TAYLOR

THE MOST IMPORTANT ATTRIBUTE IN A POKER PLAYER IS OF COURSE TO BE ABLE TO ADOPT A "POKER FACE"...

YOU MAY FEEL ALL SORTS OF EXTREME EMOTIONS AS YOU LOOK AT YOUR CARDS – JOY, TRIUMPH, NERVOUSNESS, FEAR – BUT YOU MUST ENSURE THEY ARE KEPT HIDDEN...

AT ALL TIMES YOUR EXTERIOR MUST REMAIN EXPRESSIONLESS, IMPASSIVE, DEADPAN IN ORDER TO BLUFF THAT ALL-IMPORTANT OTHER PERSON...

YOUR OPPONENT?

NO, YOUR BOSS. SO IT LOOKS LIKE YOU'RE DOING A SPREADSHEET RATHER THAN PLAYING TEXAS HOLD'EM WITH TWO GUYS IN FINLAND AND AN INSOMNIAC IN SINGAPORE...

Alex PEATTIE + TAYLOR

TOO MANY WOMEN ARE SEEKING EASY MONEY THESE DAYS BY SUING THEIR EMPLOYERS FOR SEXUAL HARASSMENT...

LET'S BE REALISTIC: WE ALL KNOW THE CITY IS AN AGGRESSIVE, DEMANDING ENVIRONMENT AND THAT THERE'S A HIGH LEVEL OF TESTOSTERONE INVOLVED...

AND, SURE, I'VE BEEN SUBJECTED TO LEWD REMARKS AND SEXIST BANTER BY MALE COLLEAGUES... BUT THE IDEA OF REPORTING THE BANK TO THE INDUSTRIAL TRIBUNAL? THAT'S LUDICROUS...

MY GOD... HER BONUS EXPECTATIONS ARE SERIOUSLY OUT OF LINE...

IS SHE REALLY HINTING SHE'S EXPECTING US TO GIVE HER MORE THAN SHE'D GET FROM TAKING THE BANK TO COURT?

Alex PEATTIE + TAYLOR

BUT WHY DO I HAVE TO PRETEND TO ALEX AND PENNY THAT WE'RE NOT GOING AWAY AT CHRISTMAS?

BONUS EXPECTATIONS MANAGEMENT, BRIDGET. IF ALEX REALISED WE WERE GOING ON AN EXPENSIVE HOLIDAY TO SOUTH AFRICA HE'D ASSUME THAT THE BONUS POOL WAS AWASH WITH CASH...

SO I GOT MY P.A. TO BOOK THE TRIP FOR US ON THE SLY... YOU SEE, SOMETIMES ONE HAS TO RESORT TO THESE ELABORATE SUBTERFUGES AND HOPE THAT THE TRUTH DOESN'T LEAK OUT TO THE WRONG EARS UNTIL IT'S TOO LATE...

SO YOUR WIFE STILL HASN'T REALISED THAT THE ENGLAND CRICKET TEAM IS TOURING SOUTH AFRICA OVER CHRISTMAS?

NO AND AS LONG AS ALEX DOESN'T KNOW I'M GOING THERE HE WON'T BE ABLE TO DROP ME IN IT WITH HER...

email: alex-cartoon@etgate.co.uk

Strip 1:

Alex — PEATTIE + TAYLOR

CLIVE'S APPOINTMENT AS HEAD OF DEPARTMENT HAS BEEN AN UNMITIGATED DISASTER...

I SAY WE HAVE NO OPTION BUT TO GET RID OF HIM IMMEDIATELY...

NOW COME ON, DAVID. LET'S NOT BE HASTY ABOUT THIS...

WE'VE GOT TO LOOK AT THE BROADER PICTURE. GENERAL BUSINESS LEVELS HAVE NOT LIVED UP TO PEOPLE'S EXPECTATIONS AND IT WAS A POOR YEAR FOR THE BANK OVERALL...

GOOD POINT.

SO WE KEEP CLIVE ON LONG ENOUGH TO PAY OUT THE DERISORY DEPARTMENTAL BONUSES AND TAKE ALL THE FLAK FOR THEM?

EXACTLY... AND <u>THEN</u> WE FIRE HIM...

email: alex-cartoon@etgate.co.uk

Strip 2:

Alex — PEATTIE + TAYLOR

SORRY I'M LATE, PENNY. I HAD REAL PROBLEMS GETTING JAKE UP AND DRESSING HIM THIS MORNING.

DON'T WORRY, CHLOE. IT MUST HAVE BEEN TOUGH FOR YOU NOT HAVING ANY DOMESTIC HELP AT THE MOMENT.

IT WAS A NIGHTMARE.

BUT YOU KNOW WHAT IT'S LIKE OVER THE FESTIVE SEASON — SOMETIMES YOU'RE FORCED TO MAKE DO WITHOUT THE AU PAIR FOR A DAY OR TWO...

AH, THERE YOU ARE MAGDA — THANKS FOR SAVING A PLACE FOR ME... NOW GET HOME AND MAKE THE BEDS...

SALE | SALE | SALE | SALE

SALE STARTS AT 10PM

CLOSED

email: alex-cartoon@etgate.co.uk

Strip 3:

Alex — PEATTIE + TAYLOR

SO HERE YOU ARE, BRIDGET... WHAT WERE YOU DOING IN THAT INTERNET CAFE?

CYBERCAFE

AFTER ALL YOU ALWAYS GIVE ME A REALLY HARD TIME IF I ATTEMPT TO DO ANY WORK WHILE WE'RE ON HOLIDAY...

I KNOW, CLIVE...

I JUST HAD TO SEND A QUICK E-MAIL TO SOMEONE. I WAITED BUT DIDN'T GET ANY RESPONSE...

MAYBE THE PERSON'S AWAY ON HOLIDAY...

OH HE <u>IS</u>... I KNOW...

BECAUSE IT WAS <u>YOUR</u> WORK E-MAIL, YET NO "OUT OF OFFICE AUTO REPLY" E-MAIL CAME BACK... SO HAND OVER THAT BLACKBERRY, CLIVE. I KNOW YOU'VE GOT IT SOMEWHERE...

email: alex-cartoon@etgate.co.uk

Strip 4:

Alex — PEATTIE + TAYLOR

WELL, TONY, I LIKE AN ANALYST WHO'S PREPARED TO RISK HIS OWN MONEY TO BACK HIS JUDGEMENT...

A FULL SIX MONTHS AGO YOU, AS OUR BANKING ANALYST, WERE SAYING THAT OUR COMPETITOR ERSATZBANK WAS IN TROUBLE — A VERDICT SUBSEQUENTLY BORNE OUT BY EVENTS...

BUT INSTEAD OF JUST PUBLISHING YOUR NOTE, YOU ALSO PRIVATELY TOOK THE OBVIOUS COURSE OF ACTION WITH RESPECT TO A COMPANY YOU DEEMED TO BE GOING DOWN THE TUBE...

YES.

I TOOK A JOB THERE, GOT MADE REDUNDANT TWO WEEKS LATER AND WALKED AWAY WITH A YEAR'S MONEY...

SO WE'D LIKE TO OFFER YOU YOUR OLD JOB BACK...

email: alex-cartoon@etgate.co.uk

Alex PEATTIE + TAYLOR

EVERYONE COMES BACK TO WORK HAVING OVERINDULGED AT CHRISTMAS, SO WE'VE ORGANISED A DEPARTMENTAL WEIGHT-LOSS COMPETITION...

PEOPLE ARE DOING THEIR WEIGH-INS NOW AND WHOEVER'S SHED THE MOST POUNDS BY MARCH WINS A PRIZE... IT'S JUST A BIT OF FUN...

TRUE, BUT INSTRUCTIVE ALL THE SAME...

AS A BOSS IT'S WORTH NOTING WHICH OF YOUR TEAM MEMBERS HASN'T BOTHERED TO SIGN UP, LIKE HUGHES THERE. IT CAN TELL YOU A LOT ABOUT A CHAP...

THAT HE'S NOT A TEAM PLAYER?

NO... THAT HE'S GOT A NEW JOB LINED UP AND IS INTENDING TO LEAVE AS SOON AS HE GETS HIS BONUS NEXT WEEK.

AH. SO BEST NOT TO PAY HIM ONE THEN?

Alex PEATTIE + TAYLOR

THE END OF THE BANK'S FINANCIAL YEAR MEANS IT'S TIME FOR JOHN TO RETIRE...

WELL, HE'S SIXTY AND FRANKLY A BIT OF A RELIC...

OF COURSE HIS HEYDAY WAS BACK IN THE 70s AND 80s WHEN THE FOUR-HOUR LUNCH WAS THE NORM. HE FEELS ALIENATED BY THE MODERN PURITANICAL CITY WHERE HALF THE PEOPLE DON'T DRINK...

STILL, IN RECOGNITION OF HIS MANY YEARS' LONG SERVICE THE BANK HAS ORGANISED THIS ALL-EXPENSES PAID RETIREMENT BASH FOR HIM.

YES.

...IN THE MONTH OF JANUARY?

JUST A PERRIER FOR ME.

ME TOO. I'M ON THE WAGON TILL FEBRUARY...

AND ME.

Alex PEATTIE + TAYLOR

I REALLY DON'T KNOW WHY YOU GO THROUGH THIS STUPID RITUAL OF GIVING UP SMOKING EVERY NEW YEAR, RUPERT.

AFTER ALL, YOU'RE ALWAYS BACK ON THE CIGARETTES BY THE END OF JANUARY. ALL IT MEANS IS THAT NICOTINE DEPRIVATION PUTS YOU IN A FOUL TEMPER FOR THE WHOLE OF THE MONTH...

I SUPPOSE IT'S TRUE, DARLING...

YOU'RE IRRITABLE, CANTANKEROUS, FRACTIOUS, SULLEN, SUBJECT TO SUDDEN MOOD SWINGS... AND THOSE AROUND YOU HAVE TO PUT UP WITH IT... I MEAN DOES IT REALLY SERVE ANY USEFUL FUNCTION?

YES... IT DOES...

...WHEN I'M TRYING TO MANAGE MY DEPARTMENT'S EXPECTATIONS...

RUPERT'S IN A FILTHY BATE AGAIN TODAY...

I SUPPOSE THAT'S AN INDICATION THAT OUR BONUSES ARE LOOKING POOR...

Alex PEATTIE + TAYLOR

THESE DAYS ALL CONVERSATIONS WITH CUSTOMERS HAVE TO BE LOGGED IN FULL ON THE CLIENT RELATIONSHIP MANAGEMENT SYSTEM...

SO WHEN I PHONE A CLIENT MY P.C. AUTOMATICALLY DISPLAYS ALL HIS DETAILS: NAMES OF KIDS, WHERE HE WENT ON HOLIDAY, EVEN THE STOCKS I'VE RECOMMENDED TO HIM.

OBVIOUSLY I WOULDN'T WANT HIM TO REALISE I'VE GOT ALL THE INFO ON A COMPUTER SCREEN IN FRONT OF ME, SO I PRETEND EVERYTHING'S DOWN TO THE POWERS OF MY MEMORY...

TAP TAP

BEFORE YOU GIVE ME YOUR STOCK PICKS FOR THE COMING YEAR, CAN YOU REMIND ME HOW YOUR LAST YEAR'S PREDICTIONS WORKED OUT?

OH I REALLY CAN'T RECALL... IT WAS SUCH A LONG TIME AGO...

email: alex-cartoon@etgate.co.uk

Alex PEATTIE + TAYLOR

WELL, DARLING, I'M GLAD YOUR BANK'S COMPLIANCE CODES FORCE YOU TO TAKE A MINIMUM OF ONE TWO-WEEK HOLIDAY A YEAR...

YOU'RE SUCH A WORKAHOLIC THAT OTHERWISE YOU'D SPEND EVERY DAY OF THE YEAR AT YOUR DESK GETTING STRESSED OUT RUNNING ALL YOUR VARIOUS TRADING POSITIONS...

BUT THE THING ABOUT BEING ON HOLIDAY IS THAT AT LEAST ONE IS ALLOWED TO UNWIND.

TRUE...

AND THE ONE I'M WORRIED ABOUT UNWINDING IS A BRAZILIAN CREDIT DERIVATIVES POSITION... MY BOSS WILL FIRE ME FOR SURE WHEN HE DISCOVERS THE LOSS I'VE BEEN HIDING.

Alex PEATTIE + TAYLOR

MUM, DO I HAVE TO WEAR BRACES? I HATE THEM...

YOU MAY HATE THEM NOW BUT YOU'LL BE GLAD OF THEM LATER...

OTHERWISE THE DAY COULD COME WHEN YOU'LL HAVE LEFT SCHOOL AND YOU'LL BE EMBARKING ON YOUR ADULT LIFE AND YOU'LL REGRET YOU DIDN'T WEAR THEM.

EVERYONE ELSE EXCEPT YOU WILL BE GOING AROUND WITH BIG CONFIDENT SMILES ON THEIR FACES AND YOU'LL BE THINKING 'OH GOD, I WISH I'D WORN MY BRACES...'

1984 — MEGABANK

CRINGE

YOUR MUM'S RIGHT, CHRISTOPHER...

Alex PEATTIE + TAYLOR

SO HOW COME WE'RE FLYING COACH CLASS FOR OUR SKIING WEEKEND, DAD?

THAT'S MY FAULT, CHRISTOPHER.

I PAID FOR THE TRIP WITH MY AIR MILES, BUT I WAS LATE BOOKING AND THERE WERE NO CLUB CLASS SEATS LEFT AVAILABLE... STILL, IT'S ONLY A SHORT FLIGHT...

FRANKLY WE'RE SO ACCUSTOMED TO BEING IN BUSINESS CLASS ENJOYING THE TRAPPINGS OF PRIVILEGE AND WEALTH THAT IT MAKES A PLEASANT CHANGE TO BE AMONG ORDINARY PEOPLE...

I FIND MYSELF ENJOYING THE COMPLIMENTARY CHAMPAGNE WE'RE ENTITLED TO MUCH MORE BACK HERE...

ENVY ENVY

Alex PEATTIE + TAYLOR

GENERAL BUSINESS LEVELS WERE POOR LAST YEAR AND THE EQUITY SALES TEAM'S BONUSES REFLECTED THIS...

HOWEVER IN VIEW OF THEIR REACTION TO THESE DISAPPOINTING PAYOUTS MAYBE WE SHOULD GIVE THEM SOME EXTRA...

AFTER ALL, BONUSES SHOULD BE USED TO REWARD THOSE WHO ARE SKILLED AT THEIR JOBS AND THESE GUYS CLEARLY ARE...

YES. LOOK AT THEM...

INSTINCTIVELY BLUFFING EACH OTHER THAT THEY ACTUALLY GOT A FORTUNE...

QUITE: SALESMANSHIP PAR EXCELLENCE...

TWO MORE MAGNUMS OF KRUG

email: alex-cartoon@etgate.co.uk

Alex PEATTIE + TAYLOR

THIS IS THE WEEK WHEN OUR DEPARTMENTAL BONUSES ARE ANNOUNCED.

IT'S NEVER TOO LATE TO INFLUENCE THE BOSS'S DECISION SO I'M GOING IN TO SEE HIM TOMORROW TO REMIND HIM JUST HOW WELL I'VE BEEN DOING MY JOB OF LATE...

AFTER ALL THE BANK PITCHES FOR LOTS OF DEALS OVER THE COURSE OF A YEAR BUT WHAT'S IMPORTANT IS HOW MANY OF THEM COME TO FRUITION AND HOW MUCH PERSONAL CREDIT ONE CAN TAKE FOR THAT...

...SO, AS I SAY, I'VE MANAGED TO STYMIE AND PUT THE KIBOSH ON JUST ABOUT EVERY BIT OF BUSINESS THE BANK'S ATTEMPTED TO DO THIS LAST YEAR...

HMM... YES... MOST IMPRESSIVE...

HEAD OF COMPLIANCE

email: alex-cartoon@etgate.co.uk

Alex PEATTIE + TAYLOR

HOW PEOPLE REACT TO GETTING THEIR BONUS CAN MAKE ONE'S JOB AS A BOSS EASIER OR HARDER...

TRUE...

MOST OF OUR PEOPLE ARE HOARY OLD HANDS WHO EXPECT TO RECEIVE A SIX-FIGURE SUM AND DIDN'T BOTHER TO HIDE THEIR DISGUST IF I AWARDED THEM ANYTHING LESS THAN THAT...

COMPARE THAT WITH THE HAPPY, CONTENTED REACTION OF OUR GRADUATE TRAINEE STEVENS, WHO'S BEEN AT THE BANK LESS THAN A YEAR AND HAD NO EXPECTATIONS OF GETTING A BONUS AT ALL...

AND SO DOESN'T UNDERSTAND THE SIGNIFICANCE OF BEING AWARDED ZERO...

I'M GOING TO HAVE TO CALL HIM IN AND EXPLAIN IT'S A HINT HE SHOULD LOOK FOR A NEW JOB...

email: alex-cartoon@etgate.co.uk

Alex PEATTIE + TAYLOR

HEY, CLIVE FANCY A DRINK TONIGHT?

ALEX, YOU'VE HAD YOUR BONUS... YOU DON'T NEED TO SUCK UP TO ME ANY MORE...

OH CLIVE! OKAY, YOU'RE MY BOSS AND IT WAS PRETTY OBVIOUS WHY I'VE BEEN MAKING A SPECIAL EFFORT TO SEE YOU SOCIALLY... BUT THAT'S NOT THE ONLY ASPECT TO THE RELATIONSHIP, IS IT?

ISN'T IT?

NO! IF I JUST CUT YOU OFF AS A FRIEND NOW AND DIDN'T EVEN WANT TO TALK TO YOU, WHAT KIND OF PERSON WOULD I BE LIKE?

THE KIND OF PERSON WHO WAS P*SSED OFF BECAUSE I'D ONLY GOT A SMALL ONE... AND I WOULDN'T WANT PEOPLE TO JUMP TO THAT CONCLUSION...

email: alex-cartoon@etgate.co.uk

Alex PEATTIE + TAYLOR

YOU SEE, SARA, BEING A BOSS IS NOT ALL ABOUT BEING HARD-NOSED AND CONFRONTATIONAL

FOR EXAMPLE ONE OF MY TEAM, TIM YEATES, WAS OBVIOUSLY DISAPPOINTED BY THE SMALLNESS OF HIS BONUS AND HAS SUNK INTO A STATE OF LETHARGY AND DEPRESSION...

THIS IS WHERE A HEAD OF DEPARTMENT HAS TO TAKE POSITIVE ACTIONS TO REBUILD THE PERSON'S SELF CONFIDENCE AS AN INVESTMENT BANKER AND MAKE HIM FEEL VALUED AND APPRECIATED...

I SEE...

SO YOU WANT ME AS A HEADHUNTER TO PHONE HIM UP AND OFFER HIM VARIOUS BOGUS JOBS?

YES... AND WHEN THEY FAIL TO MATERIALISE PERHAPS THE USELESS IDIOT WILL START APPLYING FOR SOME HIMSELF...

44

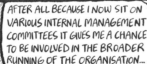

Alex PEATTIE + TAYLOR

So you're so important in the bank these days that you have TWO P.A.s RUPERT?

OH YES...

It's indispensible to a senior director, Alex. We're very busy people and can't allow ourselves to be burdened with unnecessary tasks and responsibilities...

Back in the old days when I had just one secretary there were always things that to my considerable inconvenience I'd end up having to do myself...

Such as remember her birthday?

Quite. Whereas now I can get each girl to send the other flowers from me on the appropriate day... with neither any the wiser...

email: alex-cartoon@etgate.co.uk

Alex PEATTIE + TAYLOR

We made Spencer redundant last week but he's refusing to accept our terms and go quietly...

And now I hear on the grapevine that he's considering taking the bank to the employment tribunal on the grounds of unfair dismissal...

Well, this is a standard ruse employed by one side in a dispute like this to get the other party to cave in...

I can well imagine who put this rumour about...

Well, ME obviously... the ceiling on payouts is £53,500...

And if the word is that he's prepared - for such a low sum - to blow his chances of ever working in the city again, he'll look like a total loser...

HEH HEH...

email: alex-cartoon@etgate.co.uk

Alex PEATTIE + TAYLOR

When I first started in the City 20 years ago as a junior analyst I found it most frustrating.

I might spend weeks of painstaking labour crafting a research note on a sector, knowing that the client was unlikely to give it more than a cursory flick-through.

However, things have moved on. I'm now the bank's chief economist and I no longer feel that my clients show such disrespect for my research...

Because you spend as little time writing it as they do reading it?

Quite. These days one can just cut and paste it all off company websites.

email: alex-cartoon@etgate.co.uk

Alex PEATTIE + TAYLOR

When a budget airline opens up a route to a certain French town it often encourages people to buy property there.

In the commercial world too there is frequently a direct correlation between international airline schedules and the convenience of the business traveller...

For example our bank has just signed an exclusive travel deal with Stateside Airlines. This has already helped boost Denver's popularity as a jump-off point on a trip to the U.S.A...

Because it's the one major U.S. city that Stateside's cut-price crates DON'T fly to?

Quite. Thus permitting one to book one's transatlantic flight on B.A.

email: alex-cartoon@etgate.co.uk

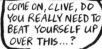

Alex PEATTIE + TAYLOR

I'M FROM M.I.N.G.L.E., THE MEGABANK INFORMAL NETWORK OF GAY AND LESBIAN EMPLOYEES...

OH YES...

I'M HERE TO PROTEST AT THE BANK'S HIGHLY SEXIST RECRUITMENT POLICY WHICH EXEMPLIFIES THE TYPICALLY RIGID, OLD-FASHIONED AND REACTIONARY THINKING OF MIDDLE-AGED MALES LIKE YOURSELF...

WELL, I'LL TELL YOU...

OF COURSE YOU'RE VERY KEEN TO BE SEEN TO BE FULFILLING DIVERSITY QUOTAS AND EMPLOYING FEMALES. BUT HOW MANY OF THESE NEW RECRUITS ARE GAY WOMEN..?

ER...

LOADS OF THEM...THAT'S BECAUSE YOU THINK WE WON'T GO OFF AND HAVE BABIES AND COST YOU A FORTUNE IN MATERNITY LEAVE, ISN'T IT?

IT MIGHT BE...

HAVEN'T YOU HEARD OF I.V.F.?...SPERM DONORS...?

Alex PEATTIE + TAYLOR

THANK YOU, MR MASTERLEY...YES, I HAVE ALL THE DETAILS OF YOUR BREAKDOWN...

BREAKDOWN RECOVERY

A RECOVERY VEHICLE IS ON ITS WAY TO YOU... NO, SIR, I'M AFRAID ALL YOU CAN DO IS REMAIN WITH YOUR CAR UNTIL OUR MAN ARRIVES... I'M SORRY, SIR...

YES, I APPRECIATE THAT YOU'RE A SENIOR BUSINESS EXECUTIVE AND I UNDERSTAND HOW FRUSTRATING THIS SITUATION MUST BE FOR YOU... NO, SIR, REALLY...

WE DON'T NEED YOU TO E-MAIL US A PHOTO OF YOUR ENGINE'S CONDITION OR SEND US A VIDEO OF LOCAL TRAFFIC CONDITIONS...

BUT THIS IS A 3G HANDSET...YOU MEAN I'VE GOT TO JUST USE IT AS A PHONE...?

Alex PEATTIE + TAYLOR

CHRISTOPHER, YOUR MOTHER AND I ARE GOING OUT NOW... IT'S GOOD TO SEE YOU WITH YOUR STUDY BOOKS OUT.

MAY I REMIND YOU THAT THE INTERNET IS TO BE USED FOR RELEVANT FACTUAL RESEARCH ONLY. I DON'T WANT YOU IN ANY CHATROOMS. AND MAKE GOOD USE OF THOSE ENCYCLOPAEDIAS I GAVE YOU...

I WILL, DAD...

REMEMBER WE PAY TO SEND YOU TO A PRESTIGIOUS UP MARKET SCHOOL AND BY APPLYING YOURSELF ACADEMICALLY NOW YOU HAVE THE CHANCE TO GIVE SOMETHING BACK TO YOUR PARENTS...

SCHOOL QUIZ NIGHT

ROUND 3 HISTORY

"Christopher, which 4 U.S. presidents were assassinated?

TEXT TEXT

Alex PEATTIE + TAYLOR

THESE EUROTRASH BANKERS LIKE CHRISTIAN MAY BE VERY BRIGHT AND HYPER-QUALIFIED BUT THEY LACK SOCIAL SKILLS...

TAXI

THEY MAY HAVE HAD A GLAMOROUS COSMOPOLITAN UPBRINGING ON THE CONTINENT AND SPEAK DOZENS OF LANGUAGES, BUT CAN THEY PERFORM AT A STANDARD CORPORATE HOSPITALITY FUNCTION?

WHEN, LIKE TODAY, WE'RE MAKING USE OF THE BANK'S DEBENTURES AND ENTERTAINING ENGLISH CLIENTS IN ENGLAND AT AN ENGLISH SPORTING EVENT.

OH YES, I USED TO WATCH BERGKAMP AT INTER WHEN I WAS STUDYING IN MILAN AND WHEN I LIVED IN MONTE-CARLO I HAD A SEASON TICKET AT AC MONACO WHEN THIERRY HENRY WAS THERE...

AH... NO ENGLISH PLAYERS...

REALLY?

NEXT TIME WE WON'T BRING HIM TO FOOTBALL...

58

Alex PEATTIE + TAYLOR

USING HUMOUR IN BUSINESS PITCHES TENDS TO BE AN ENGLISH PRACTICE.

FOR EXAMPLE THE TEUTONIC BUSINESS MENTALITY IS NOT SO ACCUSTOMED TO THE INCLUSION OF JOKES IN PRESENTATIONS ...AND WE'RE DOING AN EXTENSIVE ROAD SHOW ROUND GERMANY THIS WEEK.

WE'LL BE IN A MEETING WITH CLIENTS AND I'LL MAKE THE KIND OF CAREFULLY CRAFTED QUIP WHICH INDUCES MIRTH ON ONE SIDE OF THE TABLE BUT WILL BE MET WITH STONY-FACED SILENCE ON THE OTHER SIDE...

COME ON YOU B*ST**DS. TRY TO RAISE A SMILE AT LEAST...

I CAN'T, ALEX...

HO HO.. HA HA

WE'VE HEARD YOU CRACK THE SAME GAG AT FIFTEEN PITCHES IN A ROW...

HA HA

SLAP

Alex PEATTIE + TAYLOR

SINCE I'VE BEEN WORKING IN LONDON I'VE LEARNT TO BE MORE SENSITIVE TO ENGLISH ATTITUDES...

IN FRANCE IT'S QUITE NORMAL TO DISPLAY SYMBOLS OF YOUR STATUS PRIVILEGE AND WEALTH IN FRONT OF WORK COLLEAGUES, BUT HERE IT CAN EVOKE THE WRONG RESPONSE.

FOR EXAMPLE IT WAS CLEARLY INAPPROPRIATE FOR ME AS A GRADUATE TRAINEE TO HAVE MY OWN HAND-MADE MONOGRAMMED LUGGAGE WHICH IS WHY I BOUGHT THIS STANDARD SUITCASE INSTEAD...

SO WHEN IT'S IN THE OFFICE ON A FRIDAY NO ONE REALISES THAT IT'S YOURS?

YES AND THEY DON'T DELIBERATELY MAKE ME WORK LATE TO RUIN MY WEEKEND AWAY.

eurostar TERMINAL

DEPARTURES / DEPARTS

Alex PEATTIE + TAYLOR

WELL, CHRISTIAN, THAT ROUND OF GOLF SUMMED UP THE WIDE CULTURAL GULF THAT DIVIDES OUR NATIONS...

CHEATING, UNDERHANDEDNESS AND DISRESPECT FOR THE RULES ARE SO DEEPLY INGRAINED IN THE FRENCH PSYCHE THAT YOU SIMPLY HAVE NO IDEA HOW TO CONDUCT YOURSELF ON THE SPORTS FIELD...

BUT MAY I REMIND YOU THAT IN THIS COUNTRY WE HAVE LONG-ENTRENCHED AND IMMUTABLE PRINCIPLES THAT DETERMINE OUR APPROACH TO COMPETITIVE SPORT...

SUCH AS ALWAYS LETTING THE CLIENT WIN...

BUT IF YOU WANT HIS BUSINESS WHY DO YOU NOT SIMPLY BRIBE HIM AS WE DO IN FRANCE...?

MEGABANK GOLF DAY

Alex PEATTIE + TAYLOR

I'M AFRAID YOUR SON APPEARS TO BE GOING THROUGH A REBELLIOUS PHASE AT THE MOMENT, MR MASTERLEY...

BUT THIS IS TERRIBLE, HEADMASTER. I'D ALWAYS HOPED THAT THIS SCHOOL WOULD GIVE CHRISTOPHER THE FOUNDATION FOR A CAREER IN THE CITY...

WELL I'M AFRAID HE'S A DISRUPTIVE PRESENCE IN THE CLASSROOM. AN UNDER-ACHIEVER WHO SEEKS ATTENTION BY PREVENTING OTHERS FROM GETTING ON WITH THEIR WORK.

OH MY GOD!

IT SOUNDS LIKE HE'LL END UP WITH A JOB IN COMPLIANCE.

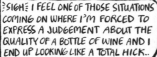

Alex PEATTIE + TAYLOR

"Hi Nick, I think I've managed to reply to all the points in your e-mail, though it's been tricky..."

"My wife is very much against me working on a Sunday (whose isn't?) and obviously I too don't like my business life to intrude into my precious downtime at the weekend. Alex."

"Hi Alex. I know what you mean about precious downtime. You mean the time you get to spend with your family, right? Nick"

"Nick, No, I meant the time I get to spend <u>away</u> from them, reading the Sunday papers in the loo. But this is the only place I can discreetly e-mail from... Alex."

ALEX! YOU'VE BEEN AGES.

Alex PEATTIE + TAYLOR

ALL THESE BUSINESS SCHOOL GRADUATES TODAY HAVE TO SPEAK NUMEROUS LANGUAGES.

IT'S AMAZING TO HEAR HOW CHRISTIAN CAN PICK UP THE PHONE TO A CLIENT FROM ABROAD AND IMMEDIATELY START JABBERING AWAY INCOMPREHENSIBLY...

YES... JUST LISTEN TO HIM...

IT'S A FAR CRY FROM OUR DAY... WHEN I GOT MY FIRST JOB IN THE CITY I ONLY SPOKE ONE LANGUAGE - THE LANGUAGE OF INTER-NATIONAL BUSINESS - ENGLISH...

THESE DAYS I'M NOT SURE I DO ANY MORE...

I KNOW... BLASTED AMERICANS....

...WE NEED TO LEVERAGE THE FRANCHISE AND MONETISE THE OPPORTUNITY...

Alex PEATTIE + TAYLOR

CHRISTIAN, I'M GOING TO NEED YOUR HELP TO PREPARE FOR THIS MEETING WITH OUR AMERICAN CLIENTS TOMORROW...

YOU'RE FLUENT IN THAT BUZZY JARGON USED IN THE BUSINESS WORLD THESE DAYS SO I'LL NEED YOU TO PUT TOGETHER THE DOCUMENTATION OUR SIDE WILL REQUIRE FOR THE MEETING...

I'M GLAD TO HEAR IT, ALEX. YOU ARE NORMALLY SCORNFUL OF MODERN BUSINESS PARLANCE AND NOW YOU WANT ME TO USE MY KNOWLEDGE OF IT TO WRITE OUR TEAM'S PRESENTATION...

IT'S NOT EXACTLY A PRESENTATION...

SO WHO'S DONE THE BULLSH*T BINGO CARDS FOR THE MEETING WITH THE YANKS?

CHRISTIAN HAS... THE FIRST PERSON TO CROSS OFF SIX BUZZWORDS WINS A BOTTLE OF CHAMPAGNE...

Alex PEATTIE + TAYLOR

PHILIPPA'S ONE OF MY BEST FRIENDS... THE PROBLEM IS THAT ALEX IS SO COMPETITIVE WITH HER HUSBAND TIM.

THE FOUR OF US GETTING TOGETHER FOR A DINNER SHOULD BE RELAXED AND STRESS-FREE, BUT ON THIS OCCASION IT PROVED UNNECESSARILY FRACTIOUS...

ALEX AND TIM LOCKED HORNS AND GOT ALL CONFRONTATIONAL AND BOASTFUL WITH ONE ANOTHER. YOU KNOW WHAT BANKERS ARE LIKE - NEITHER WANTED TO BACK DOWN AND LOSE FACE...

SO WHEN WAS THIS DINNER PARTY?

IT'S FIXED FOR JUNE 28TH 2006... FINALLY.

AH YES... BOTH OF THEM TRYING TO OUTDO THE OTHER ON WHO'S BUSIEST...

email: alex-cartoon@etgate.co.uk

Strip 1:

CHRISTIAN, WHY ARE YOU SITTING AT ALEX'S DESK?

BECAUSE HE IS OUT AT ONE OF HIS LEGENDARY LONG LUNCHES...

THIS IS HOW HE GETS ALL HIS BUSINESS IDEAS FOR HIS CLIENTS, HE SAYS.. BUT MY IDEAS — DERIVED FROM ANALYSING SPREADSHEETS - ARE JUST AS GOOD.

THE PROBLEM IS ALL OUR CLIENTS HAVE CALLER I.D. ON THEIR PHONES AND SO WON'T PICK UP CALLS FROM GRADUATE TRAINEES LIKE ME, BUT IF I TAKE ADVANTAGE OF ALEX'S ABSENCE TO DIAL FROM HIS PHONE...

ALEX MASTERLEY? CALLING FROM HIS DESK AT TEN PAST TWO IN THE AFTERNOON?!

IT MUST BE SOME SORT OF HOAX. LEAVE IT ON VOICEMAIL...

email: alex-cartoon@etgate.co.uk

Strip 2:

D.V.D., GUV? I'VE GOT ALL THE LATEST FILMS HERE...

PIRATE COPIES? NO THANKS!

THESE DAYS MOVIES ARE AVAILABLE ON BOOTLEG BEFORE THEY'RE EVEN RELEASED IN THE CINEMA HERE. ANYONE CAN ILLICITLY VIEW THEM FOR JUST A FEW POUNDS...

IT'S A DISGRACE..THE BLACK ECONOMY IS DEPRIVING GENUINE BUSINESS PEOPLE FROM REAPING THE LEGITIMATE REWARDS FROM THEIR COMMERCIAL ACTIVITIES...

PEOPLE LIKE YOU GIVING AWAY THE ENDINGS OF ALL THE LATEST MOVIES?

QUITE... SEEING THEM FIRST ON PLANES OR IN HOTELS ABROAD USED TO BE ONE OF THE PERKS OF BUSINESS TRAVEL...

email: alex-cartoon@etgate.co.uk

Strip 3:

'MORNING, ALEX. HOW WAS YOUR DRIVE INTO WORK?

EVENTFUL... I GOT INTO A RACE WITH CHRISTIAN OUR EUROTRASH TRAINEE.

HE TRIED TO CUT ME UP ON HIS CRUMMY LITTLE SCOOTER..WE HAD A TUSSLE FOR A MILE OR TWO, DOING 70 MPH ALONG THE EMBANKMENT.. WE RAN A FEW RED LIGHTS UNTIL I FINALLY LEFT HIM BEHIND ME...

WE GOT FLASHED BY THE CAMERAS SO I GUESS WE'LL GET FINES, PENALTY POINTS ON OUR LICENCES AND A HIKE IN INSURANCE PREMIUMS...BUT AT LEAST I CAN AFFORD ALL THAT, UNLIKE CHRISTIAN...

HERE HE IS NOW...

YES...ONE OF THE ADVANTAGES OF HAVING FRENCH LICENCE PLATES IS THAT I CAN'T BE TRACED TO BE SENT ANY FIXED PENALTY FINES OVER HERE...

WHAT?!

email: alex-cartoon@etgate.co.uk

Strip 4:

HAVE YOU HEARD ABOUT THESE NEW ELECTRONIC TAGS THAT WORKERS IN WAREHOUSES AND FACTORIES ARE BEING MADE TO WEAR?

KEEPING TRACK OF EMPLOYEES' WHEREABOUTS IS SUPPOSED TO ENHANCE BUSINESS EFFICIENCY BUT COULD ALSO BE USED BY MANAGEMENT TO SPY ON THE WORKFORCE... IMAGINE IF IT WAS INTRODUCED IN BANKS...

WHAT DO YOU MEAN?

WELL IF THERE WAS SOMETHING THAT EMPLOYEES LIKE US WORE THAT COULD INDICATE OUR LOCATION IN THE WORKPLACE AND WHOSE FUNCTION WAS OPEN TO CYNICAL EXPLOITATION...

AH YES...

LIKE MY TRUSTY SPARE JACKET WHICH WHEN HUNG ON THE BACK OF MY CHAIR IMPLIES THAT I AM STILL SOMEWHERE IN THE BUILDING RATHER THAN OUT AT A LONG LUNCH.

WHAT WOULD I DO WITHOUT IT?

DRAPE

email: alex-cartoon@etgate.co.uk

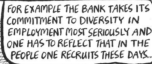

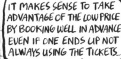

Alex — PEATTIE + TAYLOR

Panel 1: YES, WE'RE OFF TO OUR HOLIDAY HOME IN FRANCE TOMORROW FOR TWO WEEKS...

Panel 2: OF COURSE THESE BUDGET AIRLINES ARE SO CONVENIENT... WE BOUGHT OUR TICKETS THREE MONTHS AGO AND THEY ONLY COST £5 EACH FOR THE ROUND TRIP...

Panel 3: IT MAKES SENSE TO TAKE ADVANTAGE OF THE LOW PRICE BY BOOKING WELL IN ADVANCE EVEN IF ONE ENDS UP NOT ALWAYS USING THE TICKETS...

Panel 4: AHAH! JUST AS I SUSPECTED! / WHAT?

Panel 5: FOUR RETURN TICKET VOUCHERS FROM FRANCE TO ENGLAND FOR DATES OVER THE NEXT FORTNIGHT IN MY HUSBAND'S LUGGAGE... RIP RIP / IF HE THINKS HE CAN SLIP BACK TO WORK TO FIT IN A FEW MEETINGS...

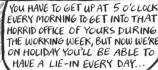

Alex — PEATTIE + TAYLOR

Panel 1: POOR MARTIN, YOU LOOK SO DRAWN, WEARY AND WORN OUT... / I KNOW, DARLING...

Panel 2: YOU HAVE TO GET UP AT 5 O'CLOCK EVERY MORNING TO GET INTO THAT HORRID OFFICE OF YOURS DURING THE WORKING WEEK, BUT NOW WE'RE ON HOLIDAY YOU'LL BE ABLE TO HAVE A LIE-IN EVERY DAY...

Panel 3: THAT'S A LOVELY IDEA, DARLING, BUT YOU KNOW HOW DIFFICULT IT CAN SOMETIMES BE TO BREAK OUT OF AN ACCUSTOMED DAILY PATTERN...

Panel 4: YOU'RE UP EARLY AGAIN, MARTIN... ZZZ... / WELL, WHEN THE HELL ELSE CAN I MAKE THESE BUSINESS CALLS WITHOUT HER REALISING I'M WORKING?

Alex — PEATTIE + TAYLOR

Panel 1: HOW'S THE HOLIDAY GOING, MARTIN? / YOU KNOW, ALEX, EVERY TIME I COME OUT HERE IT MAKES ME REALISE WHAT I'M MISSING OUT ON...

Panel 2: ONE CAN GET VERY WOUND UP WITH THE DAILY PRESSURES OF WORKING IN THE OFFICE, BUT GETTING AWAY TO THE FAMILY HOME IN FRANCE REALLY PUTS IT IN PERSPECTIVE...

Panel 3: IT'S SUCH AN AMAZING CONTRAST TO BE IN A MORE RELAXED ENVIRONMENT, FREE FROM STRESS, OF CONSTANTLY HAVING A JOB TO DO, OF BEING PERMANENTLY ANSWERABLE TO SOMEONE ELSE...

Panel 4: YES, ONLY 8 DAYS UNTIL I'M BACK THERE WITH YOU AND I CAN'T WAIT... I'M NOT EVEN ALLOWED TO WATCH THE BUSINESS NEWS OUT HERE... OOPS. HERE SHE COMES. 'BYE... / MARTIN?! TIME TO TAKE THE KIDS TO THE BEACH...

Alex — PEATTIE + TAYLOR

Panel 1: WELL, DARLING, I THOUGHT THAT DINNER PARTY AT RUPERT STERLING'S WENT VERY WELL THANKS TO YOU...

Panel 2: AFTER ALL I'M HOPING THAT HE MIGHT OFFER ME A JOB AND ONE'S PERFORMANCE IN A SOCIAL CONTEXT LIKE THAT CAN BE AN INFLUENTIAL FACTOR...

Panel 3: OBVIOUSLY EMPLOYERS ARE RELUCTANT TO TAKE ON PEOPLE IN THEIR MID 50S LIKE ME, BUT I THINK YOU MAY HAVE JUST SWUNG IT FOR ME...

Panel 4: SHE NAGGED HIM AND PUT HIM DOWN ALL EVENING. CLEARLY THEIR MARRIAGE IS ON THE ROCKS... / WELL, IF HE'S GOT A DIVORCE TO PAY FOR HE WON'T BE ABLE TO RETIRE IN A HURRY... / HMM... MAYBE I WILL OFFER HIM THAT JOB...